Desperate Dan

Crash! Bang! Wallop! What a picture! What a chaotic collection of cracking comic strips! It's action and adventure (almost) all the way, with a few slips, thrills, spills, and bottom burps thrown in for no good reason... other than laughs. And what better reason could there be?

This cartoon compendium is packed from cover to cover with a feast of favourites from the fun factory's anarchic archives. The unruly residents of Beanotown and Dandytown come together in yet another belly-busting book! There's even a sprinkling of suspense with superheroic stories featuring Bananaman, the Bash Street Super Kids, and Billy and Katie the Cats. All this and a terrorising treat as we receive an unexpected return visit from some ancient alien friends — I can't remember meeting them before? They might have called first to let us know they were coming round!

Anyway, are you sitting comfortably? Then let's begin...

© DCT Consumer Products (UK) Ltd 2023
D.C. Thomson and Co. Ltd,
185 Fleet Street,
London EC4A 2HS

Printed in the EU.

Some pages may contain references which are of their time,
but would not be considered suitable today.

THE BASH STREET KIDS

Next morning, the sun rises over Beanotown. It would have been up half an hour ago but it had a long lie in...

So, your parents went overboard in shining you up as well?

Not half.

They kept me in the bath so long I'm turning into a prune.

We'll feel better after a quick kickabout.

Yeah. Nothing like some footy to cheer you up.

DIVE!

NNNNNNNOOOOOOOOOOOOO!

Can't let you get messy.

SLIDE!

SWISH!

Eh? I missed?

If Teacher wanted a game, he only had to say.

That's grown-ups for you, mate. Never try to understand them - they're weird.

Moo-hoo-hoo.

RUB!

Billy Whizz
THE FASTEST BOY IN THE WORLD!

GEORGE vs DRAGON

Once upon a time, in a land far, far away, there lived a BRAVE and NOBLE knight, who was locked in an EPIC BATTLE with a big, FEARSOME and TERRIFYING dragon. Well, sort of...

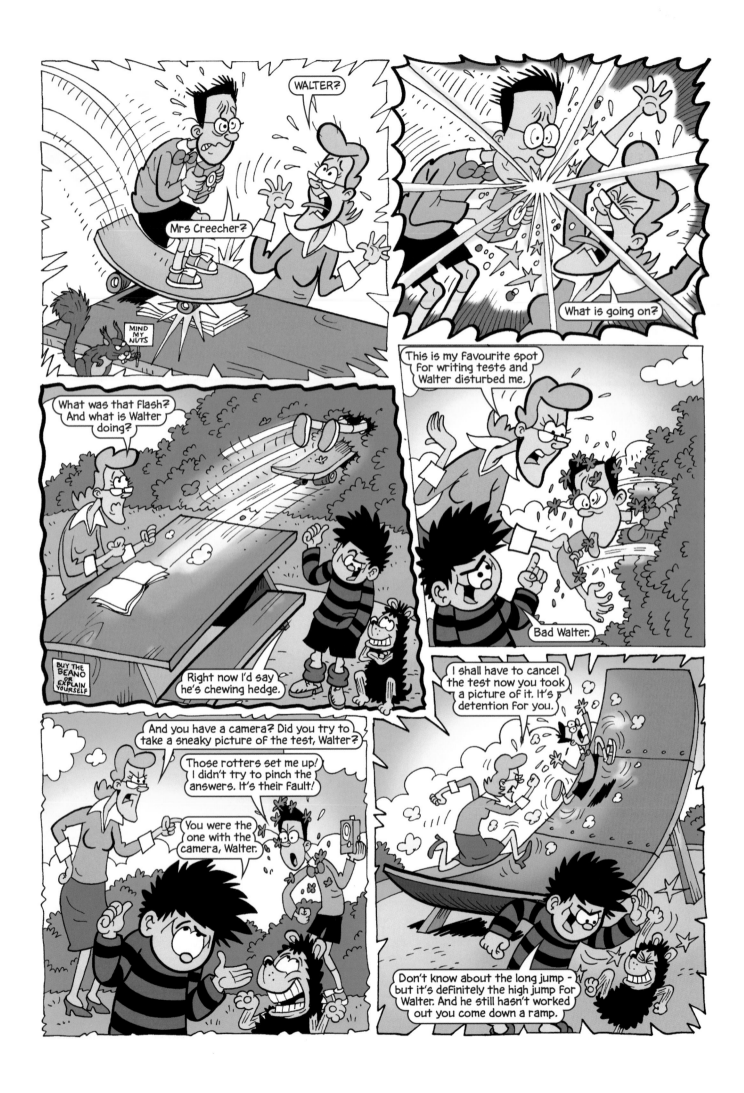

BULLY BEEF AND CHIPS!

I love fishing. It's so peaceful and relaxing.

Ha ha! Take a bath, Chips – you STINK!

Bloop!

Grrr! Bully is such a pest!

I'm not going to let him ruin my day!

What's this?

YAROO!

YANK!

Ha ha! Got you again, Chips!

I'll have the last laugh, Bully!

At last, a catch!

Hey, let me down!

Ha ha! Beefy got bitten!

YOW!

CHOMP!

SO, ONCE AGAIN, THE BASH STREET SUPER KIDS HAVE SAVED THE DAY . . . OR HAVE THEY?

DANNY! WHAT IS THE MEANING OF THIS?

ER . . . IT MEANS YOUR LESSON WAS BORING.

RANT! RAVE! READING COMIC STRIPS IN CLASS . . .! MOAN! GRIPE!

HE'S TEARING A STRIP OFF ME.

HUH! SILLY SUPERHEROES! CAN'T SEE WHAT THE KIDS SEE IN . . . HMM . . . FASTER THAN A SPEEDING BULLOCK, EH?

Daydreaming.

IF THERE'S A MATHS PROBLEM TO BE SOLVED OR A HISTORY MYSTERY . . . SEND FOR TEACHERMAN!

Upwards above...

Cooee, Mum!

FRAZZLE!

...I'm l-learning not to fly too close to the bum of any passing aeroplane! Toasty!

Some time later...

I can fly properly at last – after a lot of hard work! I wonder if there's anything Bananaman can do WITHOUT all the hard work?

Right! Silly me! Of course! He can change back to Eric again!

I didn't have to work hard to do that!

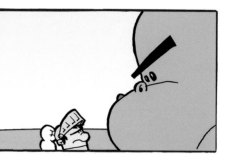

GEORGE vs. DRAGON

HE MUST BE *CRAZY* IF HE THINKS THAT WILL STOP US!

HAH! HE'S RUNNING OUT OF PLACES TO GO!

HEY, LOOKS LIKE YOU COULD USE A *HAND* THERE, PAL!

HOW DID YOU?..

NO! GIVE ME YOUR *HAND*... QUICKLY!

KREEEK!

KRAAASH!

AGGHH!

Continued later in this book

CUDDLES and DIMPLES

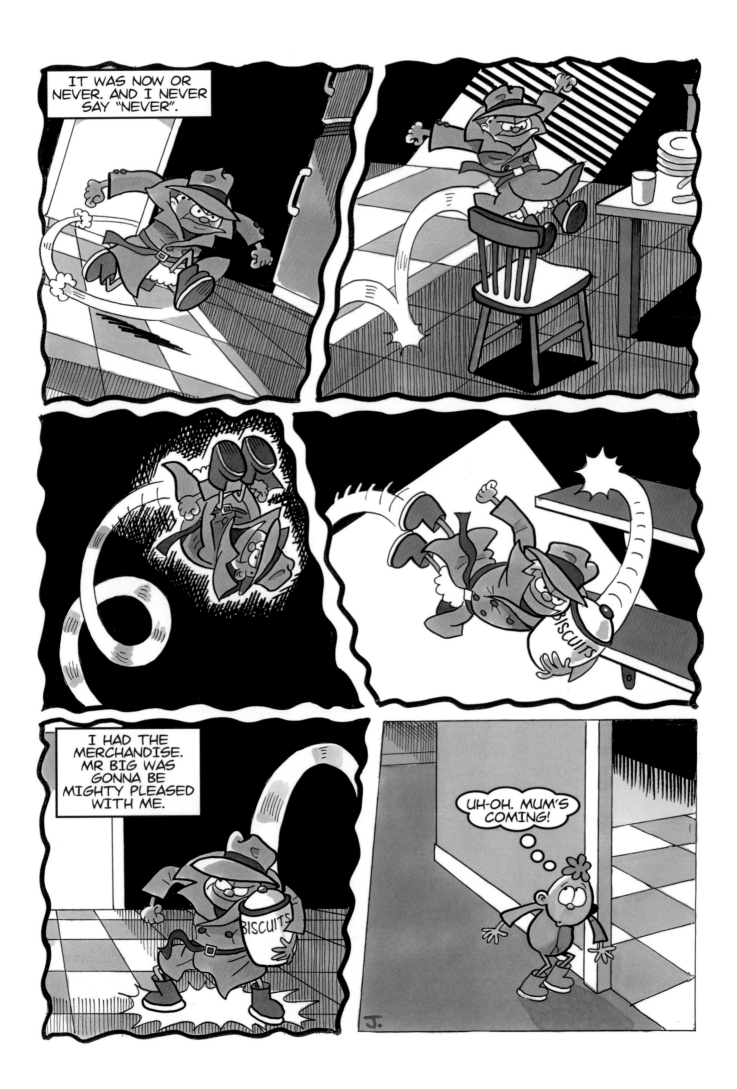

EVERY TODDLER FOR HIMSELF!

WHAT ARE YOU TWO...

..UP TO? CUDDLES!

BISCUITS

REACH FOR THE SKY, BABYFACE!

THE HEAT! LOOKS LIKE MY LOOKOUT LOOKED OUT ALRIGHT - FOR HIMSELF!

YOU'RE GOING DOWN, BABYFACE. AN' I'M GOING UP - TO SERGEANT!

THE DAME WAS HAVING A GOOD DAY - PITY I WAS PAYING!

MY HANDS WERE REDDER THAN A BABOON'S BUTT.

NAME CUDDLES

11774

NIGEL PARKINSON

PINKY'S CRACKPOT CIRCUS

AGENT DOG 2-ZERO

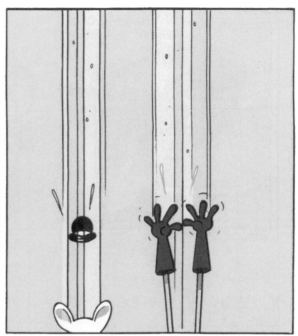

BULLY BEEF AND CHIPS!
I love paintball!
I'm sure I heard a twig snap!
KLANG!
PAINT
YOW!
Got you, Chips!
PAINT
You're not meant to use paint in a TIN, you meathead!
PAINT
Coo! Fancy that!
Is THIS better?
PAINT
Uh-oh!
OVER HERE, TROOPERS!
I just blend in, thanks to Bully's green paint!
Eek!
AAARRGGHH!!!

Continued From earlier in this book

MAYBE WE CAN GET SOME ANSWERS FROM THE *INTERNET.*

I *STILL* SAY WE CAN GET ALL THE ANSWERS WE NEED ONCE WE CATCH *LAZARUS!*

HEY, THAT'S *LAZARUS...* BUT WHO'S THE *OTHER* GUY?

IT SAYS HERE THAT SCOTT LAZARUS HAS A *BROTHER* CALLED *MIKE.* THEY WERE ONCE A *DOUBLE ACT* HEADING FOR THE *BIG TIME.*

BUT THEN, SUDDENLY, THEY *SPLIT UP...*

I THINK WE OUGHT TO HAVE A LITTLE *CHAT* WITH THIS *MIKE.* IT TURNS OUT HE WORKS FOR A LOCAL *BUILDING CONTRACTOR.*

BUT WE ALREADY *KNOW* SCOTT IS OUR MAN!

I'M BEGINNING TO THINK YOU HAVE A *CRUSH* ON THAT IDIOT!

THAT'S RIDICULOUS!

WHATEVER.

ANYWAY, I'LL SEE YOU IN THE MORNING.

 ARLY THE NEXT DAY.

HE'S LOOKING *OLDER* BUT THAT GUY LAYING BRICKS IS *MIKE LAZARUS,* ALL RIGHT!

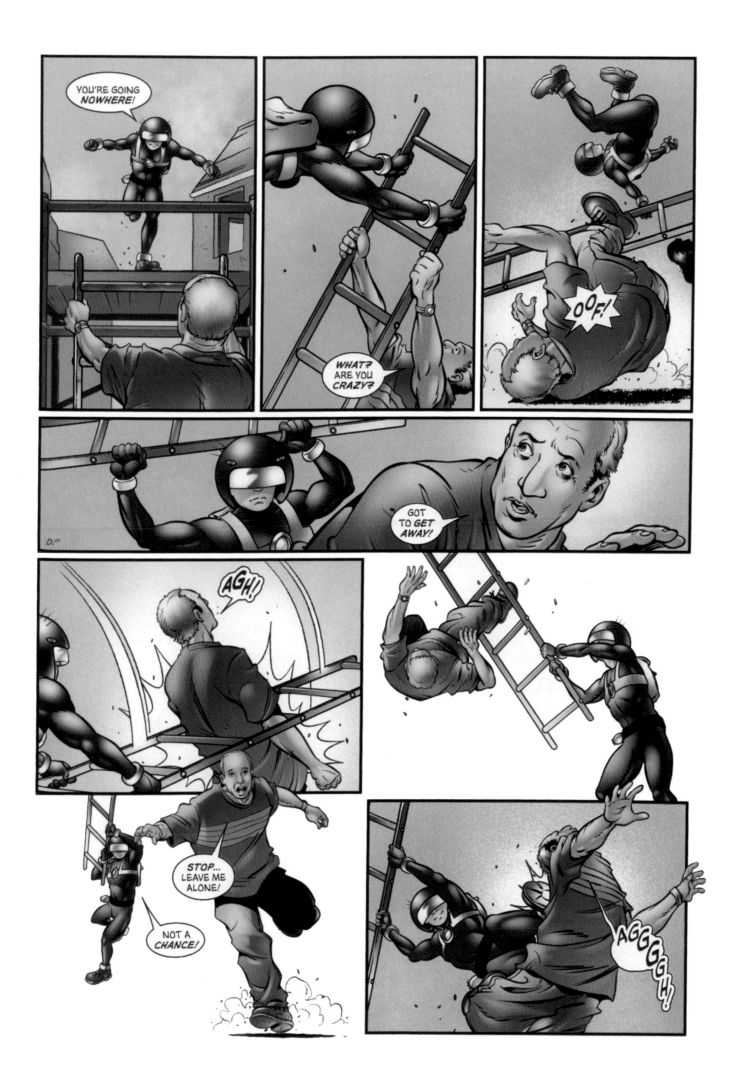

BLINKY'S MAD MOVIES

20th CENTURY HAMSTER

presents

Robin Hood

starring Blinky as ROBIN HOOD

MY POOR, DEAR ROBIN HAS BEEN INJURED AND SOON MUST DIE. ALAS, WOE AND MORE WOE!

IF THAT DOESN'T GET ME AN OSCAR NOMINATION, NOTHING WILL, NOW GET ME A BETTER PAYING JOB, AGENT BOY!

MEANWHILE BACK IN THE FILM –

LADS, I HAVE NOT LONG TO LIVE. BURY ME WHERE MY ARROW LANDS.

AND –

TWANG!

ERM ... WANT TO TRY THAT AGAIN?

AND AGAIN? AIM FOR THE WINDOW OR WE BURY YOU ON TOP OF THE WARDROBE!

FIN

JAK & TODD

GEORGE vs. DRAGON

I have SLAIN the dragon!

My HERO!

HAPPY DREAMS!

Z

GEORGE'S KIP

But then...

DING DONG! DING DONG!

OOH! There's someone at the door!

LEAP!

George's dog, Sir Barksalot.

BARK!

DING DONG! DIN—oh! There you are! I've got a parcel for you, Mr. George!

TA!

YESSSS! My dragon disguise kit is here!

SLAM!

Rilllp!

DRAGON DISGUISE KIT

)))

Kick!

And it only took three years to get here!

I'm going to try it on RIGHT NOW!

DAD

CENSORED!

And so...

PERFECT! This will fool that stupid dragon!

I'm so smart!

Hee-hee! Now to go and find that pesky dragon!

Medieval Mirth!

DRAGON'S DEN

AH-HA!

There's the beast's foul lair — now to just wait until he returns...

I'M OUT

...This'll be SO good!

Then...

HOI, FELLAHS! I've found us a DRAGON!

YIKES!

GET HIM, LADS!

Yeah!

Spin!

I'm not a real dragon, you BERKS! Leave me alone!

STAMPEDE!!

Thanks for the tip-off, big green knight! We'll soon catch that dragon!!

HELP!

Happy to help, sire! Chuckle!

YE KNIGHT DISGUISE KIT

FANTON

NICK KELLY
Special Agent

CEDRIC
And his assistant · *In* · *Agents of Change!*

Ah, Agent Kelly and Cedric. I have an important mission for you both.

These two vans are full of new-fangled weapons from our experimental weapons division...

I need you to drive them to our high security warehouse.

The last thing we need is enemy agents getting hold of them.

Okay, Cedric. I'll take the lead van, you follow me. Okay?

Okay. Just one thing...

Where's the other van?

SPACE!!!

Stolen!!!

Enemy agents!

Quick! After them!

SCREECH!

Ha ha! A clean getaway! Those British fools will soon discover their flat tyres!

Flat tyres?

I was supposed to let the tyres down on the other van, wasn't I?

That's the trouble with identical vans. Ours isn't faster.

I'll see what we have in the back to slow them down.

I don't know what any of these things do!

Just try anything!

So Cedric tries something...

ZAP!

Nigel Auchterlounie

The Bash Street Kids in "BOXING NOT SO CLEVER!"

THE END

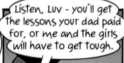

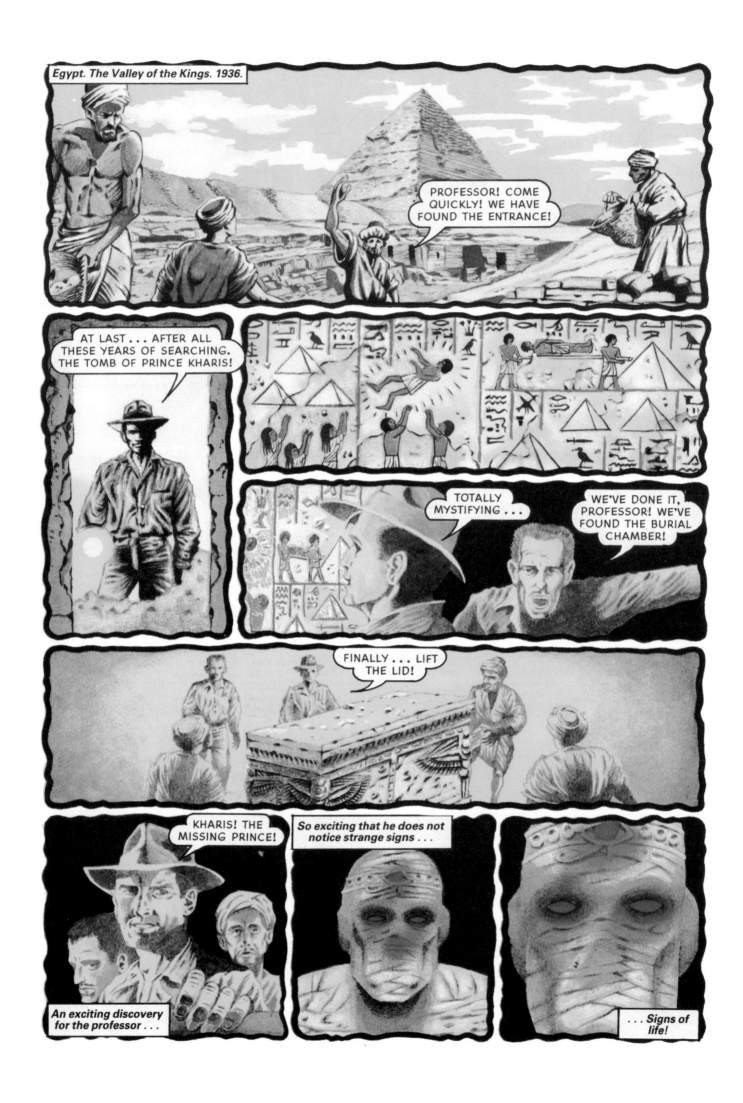

THANK YOU, GRAHAM. I'M ON MY WAY!

And, almost sixty years after he first found the mummy . . .

. . . the professor is ready to do it all over again.

While, at the scene of the crime . . .

CHECK THE STAIRS. THE ROBBERS MIGHT STILL BE IN THE BUILDING.

← STAIRS

LIGHTS MUST HAVE GONE . . . I'D . . . HEY! WHO'S THAT HIDING UP THERE?

DON'T MOVE! I'M ARMED!

I SAID DON'T . . . OH, NO! NO!!

STAY BACK! AAAARGH!!

BLAM BLAM

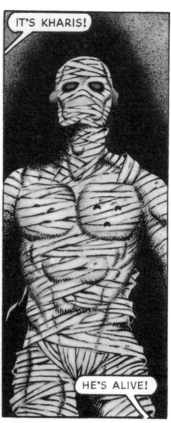

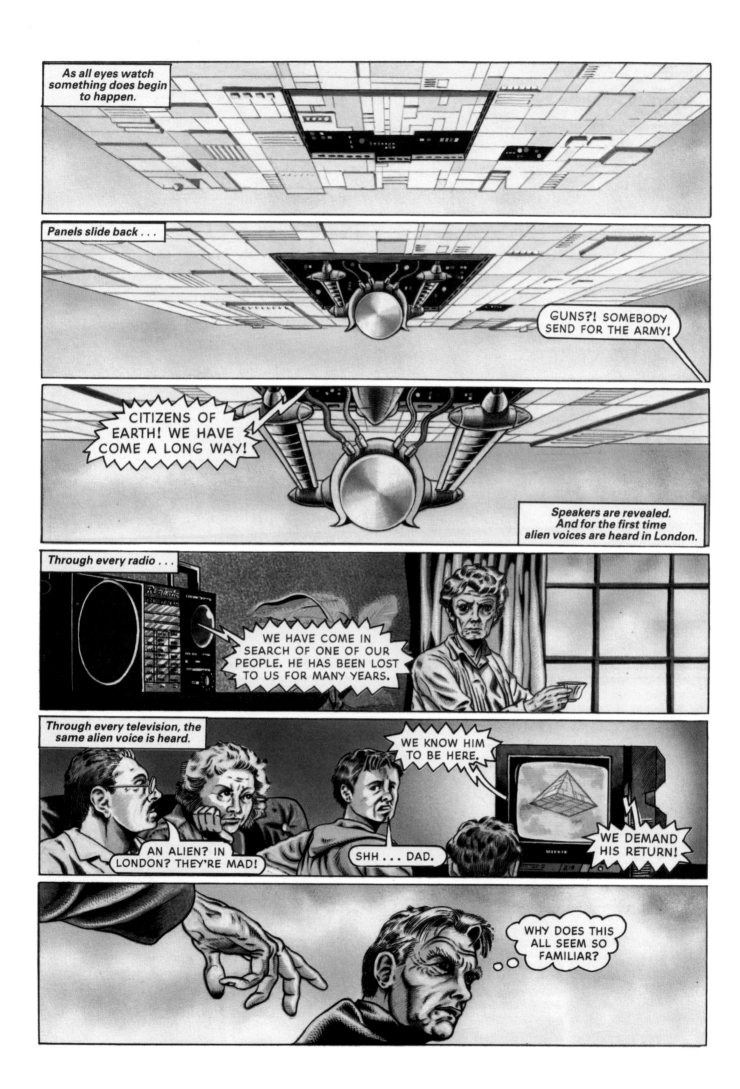

And for the first time human beings stand within an alien space craft!

GREETINGS, EARTH PEOPLE. I AM HORUS.

I KNOW!

AND I ALSO RECOGNISE ISIS, OSIRIS AND ANUBIS... THE EGYPTIAN GODS!

NOT GODS. MERELY VOYAGERS.

WE VISITED YOUR WORLD THOUSANDS OF YEARS AGO.

YES. IN EGYPT, WHERE ONE OF YOUR CREW MEMBERS WAS INJURED AND WRONGLY ENTOMBED!

...THERE IS ONE THING...

And...

WHERE ARE THEY GOING?

THEY'RE LEAVING!

WE'LL COME BACK...SOON.

And for two young minds and one not so young, all eager to learn...

...A whole new universe is opened up for them!

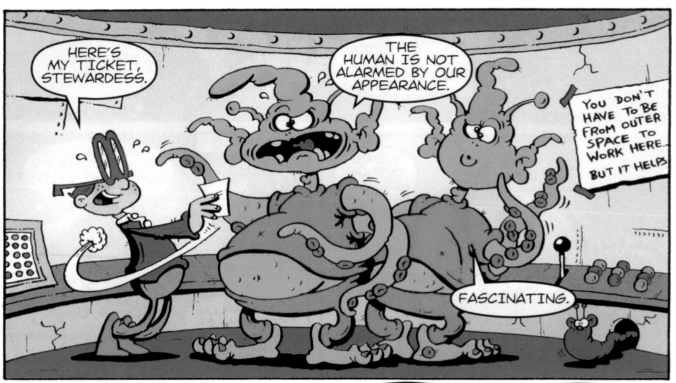

BULLY BEEF AND CHIPS!

GEORGE vs. DRAGON

ZOMBIE OLYMPICS IS OUT TODAY!

IT'S THE BEST GAME OF THE YEAR!

BUT—

JUST ZOMBIE OLYMPICS, PLEASE.

I'M SORRY – THIS GAME IS NOT FOR SALE TO CHILDREN.

WHAT? YOU'RE A ZOMBIE, YOU MEAN!

I CAN'T BELIEVE WE CAN'T PLAY ZOMBIE OLYMPICS BECAUSE WE'RE NOT OLD ENOUGH!

I KNOW, IT WAS MEANT TO BE THE BEST GAME OF THE YEAR!

LOOK AT IT! CAN'T YOU JUST IMAGINE BEING IN THE GAME?

ZOMBIE OLYMPICS

WHOA! I HAD TOO MUCH SUGAR ON MY CORNFLAKES THIS MORNING!

NO YOU DIDN'T! I SEE IT TOO!

CALAMITY JAMES

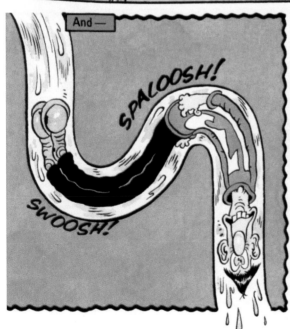

The BASH STREET SUPER KIDS

UP, UP AND WAHEY!

LOOKS LIKE IT'S A CHEMISTRY LESSON TODAY.

HOW CAN YOU TELL?

SO . . . NOT THE GREEN AND THE RED, THEN?

DANNY! WHAT HAVE YOU DONE?

BOOM!

THAT'S HOW! EITHER THAT OR OLIVE'S PUT CURRY ON THE LUNCH MENU AGAIN.

AS LONG AS SHE DOESN'T PUT IT ON A PLATE. YEUCH! MY TONGUE'S JUST OUT OF ITS SPLINT!

FLAME RETARDENT

Readers with gentle stomachs can stop quaking, it's not the curry, it's a science lesson. Readers with delicate nerves, however, watch out!

NO, FREDDY, YOU'RE SUPPOSED TO ADD CHEMICAL 'X' TO SOLUTION 'Y', NOT ADD FLOUR AND EGGS, SPRINKLE WITH SUGAR AND BAKE TILL GOLDEN BROWN.

SLURP!

NOW, WAS I SUPPOSED TO ADD THE GREEN STUFF TO THE RED STUFF OR THE YELLOW STUFF TO THE BLUE STUFF? AND IS IT SUPPOSED TO SMELL OF OLD SPORTS SOCKS?

STIR

POUR

I DON'T KNOW, BUT IT DOESN'T LOOK GOOD.

UGH! IT DOESN'T SMELL GOOD EITHER! YECK! SPORTS SOCKS!

WELL, I'VE CHECKED ALL MY SCIENCE BOOKS . . . THE FOURTEEN I'VE BROUGHT WITH ME, ANYWAY . . .

AND . . .?

FIZZ THROB

PULSE

IT LOOKS TO ME LIKE A DIMENSIONAL PORTAL THAT'LL TRANSPORT A PERSON FROM OUR REALITY INTO A DIFFERENT PLANE OF EXISTENCE!

AND IT ISN'T ANYTHING KNOWN TO SCIENCE!

THROB

HIGGS

BEANO

I DON'T BELIEVE IT!

YEAH! SMIFFY USED A FULL SENTENCE. AND HE USED WORDS, TOO!

YOU RECOGNISE IT?

I READ ABOUT IT IN MY COMIC . . . OKAY, SOMEBODY HAD TO ACTUALLY READ THE WORDS TO ME . . .

BEANO

CHUCKLE! SILLY IDEA!

NEVER UNDERESTIMATE THE POWER OF COMICS! OTHER DIMENSION, HERE I COME!

WIPE!

LEAP

SPLOOSH!

BEANO

Dear readers, do not try this at home, no matter what dimension you happen to live in!

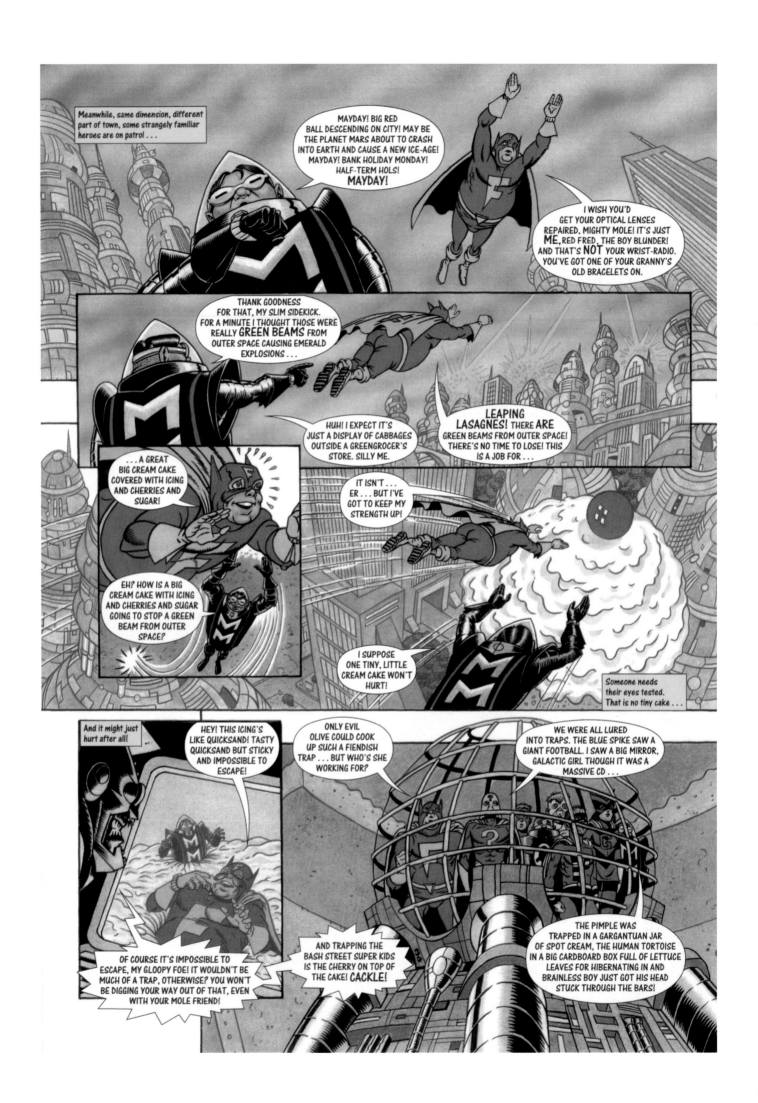

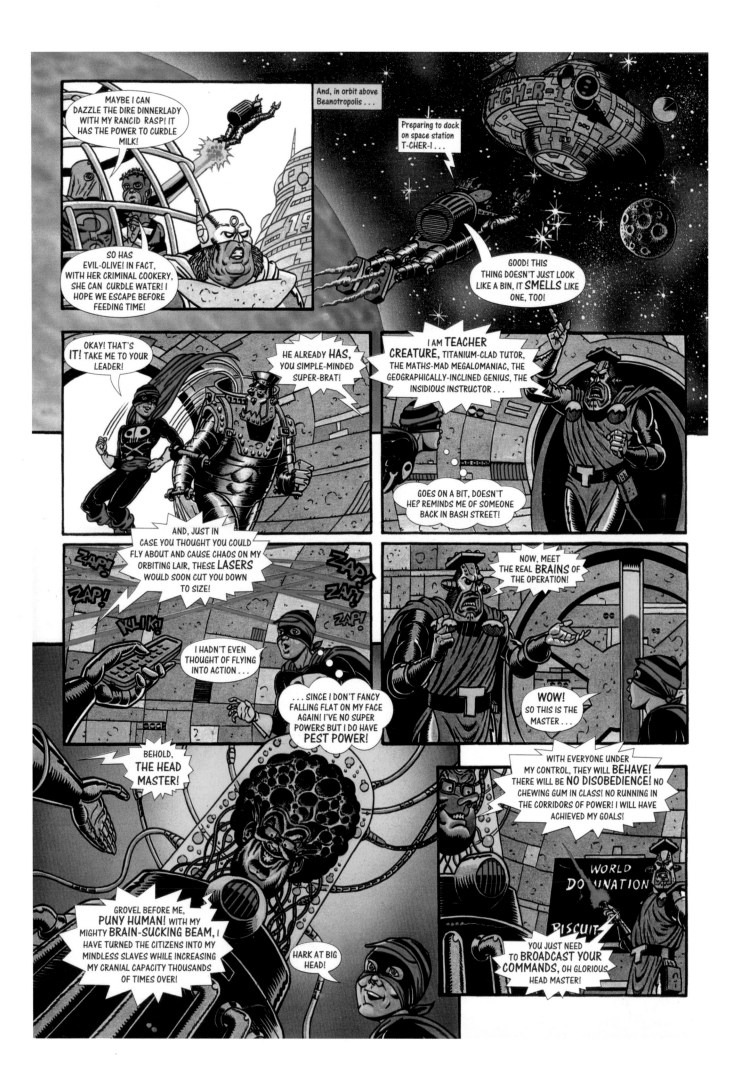

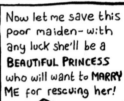

And we'll be back too! There are always more laughs to be had here at Beano HQ, and we're already working (if you can actually call it work) on more crazy collections from our fun-filled files.

Can't wait? Why wait? Laugh yourself silly every week with all your Beano pals. You can find us online at beano.com, and the weekly Beano is crammed full of jokes, japes, action, and adventures, all designed to help your days go with a BANG!